Jonathan Rhymes

Colton,

Read lots of books,
Learn new things, and
Be kind to your
teachers.

Kamili Leath

Feb. 2022

Kamili Choma Leath

This Book belongs to...

Colton

Colton

Jonathan loves to rhyme. He rhymes all the time.

Jonathan rhymes in the morning. He rhymes at night. He rhymes by the pale moon light.

Jonathan rhymes with his mother. He rhymes with his father. He even rhymes with his sister and brother.

Jonathan rhymes in the living room. He rhymes in his bedroom even when he has no headroom.

Jonathan rhymes at home. He rhymes at school. In the summer he rhymes in his cool pool.

Ted fed his red pet, Ned,
and put him to bed
with a cloth on his head.

Jonathan rhymes at the playground. He rhymes in the park after dark on a lark.

Jonathan rhymes at the lake. He rhymes at the beach with a peach in reach.

Jonathan rhymes on his bike. He rhymes in a car whether going near or far.

Jonathan rhymes on the bus without a fuss and he doesn't "cuss".

Jonathan loves to rhyme. He rhymes all the time.

This book is dedicated to my family, especially my son, Jonathan, who loved to rhyme as a preschooler. He was so excited by his new skill and shared it with me often. One day he couldn't wait until my shower was over and the idea for this book was born.

**Stay tuned for *"Jonathan goes to Ethiopia"* coming December 2021 **

About the Author

Kamili Oluseyi Choma Leath is an Early Child Care and Education professional. She has over 25 years in the field. She believes that every child can thrive in the right learning environment. She has spent her professional career helping make that belief a reality. Kamili conducts seminars; workshops and training for child care institutions and churches as well as businesses. She received a Bachelor of Arts in Psychology from Arcadia University and a Master of Science in Christian Counseling from Carin University.

Together with her husband, Jonathan M. Leath, she co-founded Discover HOPE, a youth leadership, and development organization that helps young people develop their character and cultivate integrity. Kamili is also the COO of Leath & Associates, LLC, a Cultural Competency & Educational Consultant, and a licensed insurance agent. She has been married to Jonathan for nearly 24 years. Together, they are the proud parents of four children: Jael Alicia, Jonathan Choma, Joshua David, and Joel Oluseyi.

Contact Kamili at koleath@gmail.com or on her Linked In

https://www.linkedin.com/in/kamili-leath/

Made in the USA
Monee, IL
06 December 2021

82941906R00017